THE BE
OF MY LIFE

Book 1: Getting Diabetes

by Jed Block

Illustrated by Caitlin Block

The Best Year of My Life
Book 1: Getting Diabetes

Copyright ©1999 by Jed Block
4300 Knollwood Lane
Appleton, WI 54913-6307
www.jedblock.com
jed@jedblock.com

Design by Adstaff, Neenah, Wisconsin
Printed by N.E.W. Printing, Appleton, Wisconsin

Library of Congress Catalog Card Number: 99-90681

ISBN 0-9672728-0-7

For
Stinky Good Breath,
hero

Every child is an artist.
The problem is how to remain
an artist once he grows up.
Pablo Picasso

FOREWORD

She fainted during school pictures.

She wet the bed two or three times.

She'd get up in the middle of the night to drink water.

Before school, she had a tendency to lay down on the couch and say she didn't feel good. But I attributed that to the new school she was going to.

Finally, we made a doctor appointment.

On the morning of the appointment, she said she didn't feel good again. I was preoccupied with a deadline. I took her to school and told her to call if she needed me. I said she had to start going to bed earlier. Then I went back to work.

That afternoon, the doctor told us she had diabetes. When I went to write the word, I didn't even know for sure how to spell it.

While we waited for more test results, she snuggled in my arms on my lap. She made herself stop crying, even though she was only seven.

She asked what she had done wrong. Did she eat too much candy? Was she going to have to miss piano lessons and gymnastics? When it was her birthday, she said she knew already what she was going to wish for.

I told her that if I could make her wishes come true, I'd make them so, more than anything else.

They checked her in the hospital. In no time, she was happy, inspecting things, straightening up the room. It was her room. Like a motel room. She mastered the TV. They gave her a list of videos that were available. She read the list, singing out almost every title.

I said I couldn't believe how strong she was being. A tough cookie.

Driving home, to pick up things to bring back to the hospital, I wept. For the first time in a long time, I cried like a child. Was this a wake-up call? Why did our baby have to pay the price? Is she ever going to be able to be a kid again? What is she going to do when all the other kids on her T-ball team rush to get a treat after the game?

The heck with deadlines. That's when she started being a hero. And she had no choice.

***

This is a storybook that is meant to be happy and inspirational. It's meant for adults to read, as well as children. It's meant for parents to read to and share with their children.

It's about a setback, hope and resilience.

JB

Hi, my name is Caitlin. Last year, I was diagnosed with diabetes.

It's not so bad. I still have lots of fun, and I can hardly remember not having diabetes.

This year, for third grade, I have the best teacher I ever had. Her name is Miss Flowers.

Last year, I thought Mrs. Gerald was the best teacher I ever had. She came to visit me in the hospital and gave me a beautiful, stuffed kitty with long, soft fur that really seems real. The kitty always sits on my bed, and I named her Julie, after Mrs. Gerald.

My dad said that maybe next year's teacher will be the new, best teacher I ever have. He said that's when he can tell he has it good -- when each year is better than the last one.

So far, this is the best year I ever had in my life.

Miss Flowers. Me. 1.

When I found out I had diabetes, I was in the hospital for a whole week. I was glad when I got out and got to be home with my mom and dad, and sisters, and our dog, Copper. I also wanted to go back to school.

But when I think back, the hospital was pretty fun. It was like having my own hotel room. I had my own TV, VCR and bathroom. My dadders slept every night in my hospital room on a roll-away bed. He said we bonded.

I had some real good nurses, too. My favorite was Fran. She was there with Grandma and Grandpa B when Dadders had to go to work. Fran walked with me in the halls for exercise, and we talked a lot. She also was the first nurse to check my blood sugars and ketones.

During the first night, after I changed into a hospital gown and tried out the TV, Fran gave me a big list of movies I could watch for free. Dadders and I watched movies all week.

Now, when we go to see Dr. Terry for my three-month checkups, we sometimes go into the hospital part of the building to look in "my room" and visit Fran. She's still nice.

This summer, when we visited Fran after my checkup to get ready to go back to school, Fran said there was a boy my age who just found out he had diabetes.

We went into his room to visit him. His name was Ryan, and he was sad, like I had been when I was diagnosed. He was real skinny, like I had been, too.

At first, Ryan was shy and didn't want to talk. But after my mom and dad talked to his mom and dad about diabetes not being so bad, Ryan showed me a board game that Fran had gotten out for him.

By the time we left, Ryan was at least smiling. Now, he's one of my friends at the diabetes support group.

Ryan.

3.

After Dr. Terry told us that I had diabetes, I had to have another test.

While we waited for the results, I sat on my dad's lap and wondered what I had done wrong. "Did I eat too much candy?" I asked.

Dadders told me that I didn't eat too much candy and that eating candy doesn't cause diabetes. He said diabetes just happens to some people. It's a disease, like measles, only diabetes doesn't go away...yet. "But it's something that we can take care of," Dadders said.

"Am I going to have to miss piano lessons and gymnastics?" I asked.

"Maybe this week, but you'll be able to go next week," he said.

"When it's my birthday, I know what I'm going to wish for," I said.

Dadders said that if he could make my wishes come true, more than anything, that's what he'd do.

I noticed there were tears in his eyes, too.

The reason we went to the doctor in the first place was that I fainted during picture day at school.

We were having our class picture taken on the risers in the library. We were all stuffed in there, and it was very hot. We had to stand around and wait a long time. I was sweating and felt sick to my stomach.

I must have fallen down. When I woke up, Mr. Eichelbarger, our principal, was kneeling next to me, cooling my forehead with a wet paper towel.

It was hot, confusing and pretty scarey.

My mom made a doctor's appointment right away because I also had wet the bed twice that week.

At first, Mommers and I didn't tell anyone about wetting the bed because I hadn't had an accident since I was a baby, and I was embarassed.

Mommers also said I looked skinny. When I had come into the kitchen in my underwear and T-shirt one morning, she said I looked way too skinny.

My mom is a teacher at another elementary school, and it's hard for her to get off work. That's why Dadders took me to the doctor. In the car, he said maybe I had some kind of infection.

Mom.

Dr. Terry.

After I was checked into the hospital, we had a lot of meetings to learn about all sorts of things.

First, we met Nancy, our diabetes educator. She's nice, too. She told us about diabetes and answered any questions we wanted to ask. What I like about her is that she talks to me and asks me questions, just as much as she does with Mommers and Dadders.

Nancy showed us a machine, a glucose monitor, that you use to measure the amount of sugar in your blood. She gave me a test and showed me how to use the machine, so I'd be able to do the tests myself.

You have to poke your finger to get a tiny blood sample to put on the machine. The poke hurts a little, but not very much, so I really don't mind because it's just something you have to do before meals and at bedtime. But sometimes, I get tired of it.

Checking in the hospital.

I like the monitor, though. It's a little computer. I'm known as the "mechanic" in the family, and the monitor is something to figure out, which is fun for me.

Nancy also showed us how to give shots.

At first, only the nurses gave me shots. Then it was time for Mommers and Dadders to give them.

We also had to learn about insulin. Insulin is what you have to get shots of when you have my kind of diabetes, which is called Type 1 or insulin-dependent diabetes.

The shots were the scariest part, but you get used to them, too. Mommers and Dadders watched Nancy. They practiced on a doll. Then they gave practice shots of saline solution to each other. I watched them closely, and they didn't seem to hurt each other with the shots.

They said that by getting shots, and even testing their blood sugars, they understood better what I was going through. They said that giving shots was easier than they thought it would be.

Nancy said if we all felt comfortable about it, Mommers or Dadders could give me my next shot. Nancy also gave us a diabetes video to watch and a workbook for me to do, if I wanted.

y dad was the first person in the family to give me a shot because it was at bedtime, and everyone else had gone home. We were both pretty nervous about it. But the first one he ever gave me was a good shot because it hardly hurt at all.

Mommers gave me her first shot the next afternoon, when she came to stay with me after her school. She did a good job, too.

My nervous dad.

Jean is the nutrition educator. She met with us a long time in the hospital to teach us about eating right. She's nice, too. She knows what I'm going through because she got diabetes when she was a little girl.

Jean told us about what kinds of foods I should eat to help control my diabetes. She showed us how to count the carbohydrates in food and how many I should have for meals and snacks. When you know the number of carbohydrates – I call them carbs – you know how much insulin to take. Now, whenever Mommers cooks, she knows how many carbs are on my plate.

By eating right and exercising, Jean said I'd probably be the healthiest person in the family. She also said I might help everyone else be healthier, too.

The best thing is that I can still eat the foods I like, even candy or cake, if I adjust other parts of my diet or my insulin shots.

Me.   Jean.

When I got out of the hospital, I was kind of nervous about going back to school. Even though the kids in my class had made a big, nice card for me, and everybody signed it and wrote me notes, I was afraid they would think I was different.

On the first day back, Nancy (my diabetes educator), Dadders and I met with my teacher, the principal, the school nurse and the secretary who works in the office. We had a meeting early in the morning before school started to set up a plan for taking care of my diabetes.

We brought in notes and booklets for people to read. We talked about procedures to follow just in case something happened. We also brought in supplies and some nutritious snacks for me to eat before morning and afternoon recesses. I'm also supposed to drink a juice box or have a snack when my blood sugar gets low.

11.

After our meeting was over, it was time for school to start, and Nancy came to our classroom.

She explained diabetes to all the kids in my class. She made me feel better and made all of us laugh. She also told everyone that they couldn't catch diabetes from me. She said diabetes was just a special thing about me that could be taken care of. Then she answered any question that anybody wanted to ask.

I'm glad Nancy came to school. Now, I kind of enjoy being a special person, showing everybody things about diabetes.

Halloween was my first big challenge after getting diabetes. Halloween is my third favorite holiday, and I love going trick-or-treating. But, of course, all the candy presented a problem.

Mommers and I thought about me being the person who gave out all the treats to kids who came to our house. That would be fun to do some time. But this year, I really wanted to get dressed up and go out with my friends.

I decided to be a vampire. Mommers and I agreed that I would get to keep four treats. The rest, I would split up between my sisters, Stretch and Niner.

My friends and I had a blast! We stayed out even longer than Stretch and Niner, and my bag was the fullest. I picked out my four favorite treats and got to eat one each day. The rest of the candy, I gave to my sisters. They really thanked me for it. I found out it's a lot of fun to give, and this was my best Halloween ever!

Vampire.

To keep your diabetes under control, it's important to exercise. I'm supposed to exercise every day.

During school, we have gym class and recess every day. In summer and winter, baseball and gymnastics are my favorite ways to exercise. I also like basketball, but I'm not on a team yet. We play in our driveway, though. I can already beat my sister Niner in Horse sometimes, and she's one of the best players on her basketball team. I have this hot spot from where I can almost always make a basket, and Niner's not very hot from there.

I got into gymnastics because of a movie I saw about a girl who made the Olympics gymnastics team. That's one of the things I'd like to do some day. I also want to be an ice skater, a teacher, an actress and a singer.

Gymnastics is hard, but it's fun and gives you a good workout. My dad drives me to the class. He says he respects me for it because I go all by myself, and I don't really know any of the other girls in the class.

Dadders says because of my diabetes, I'm more independent than most kids. He says I've learned to take care of myself by

Playing catch.

having to test my blood sugar all the time and give myself shots.

Not long after I came home from the hospital, I started giving myself my own shots. I use an injector to give them.

Let's face it -- sometimes the shots just plain hurt. I used to get mad at my mom and dad when the shots they gave me hurt. Then we found out about the injector. You put the syringe in it, place the injector on the spot where you want to give the shot, and push a button.

The shot goes in real fast. Sometimes it hurts, but most of the time, it doesn't. And if it hurts, at least I'm the one who's doing it, and I don't get mad at my mom and dad.

With the injector, you also don't have to watch and wait for the shot to go in. You just push the button, and it goes in fast. I really like that.

The Injector.

It's Christmas day, and we're on our way to Polo, Illinois. That's where my Grandma and Grandpa H live and some of my cousins. They live on a farm that is close to this little town of Polo.

I love going to Polo. This is where we always come for Christmas, Easter and Thanksgiving. We usually come for a week in the summer, too. There are a lot of things to do and play on the farm, and all of my cousins to play with. It's a blast!

This is one of my favorite Christmases. I love my mom and dad so much. I love my sisters. I love Copper. I can't wait until we get to Polo.

Cedar Crest Farm

Grandma H is one of the best cooks ever. So is Grandma B. But the food that Grandma H makes is different. It's farm food. It's like it's old-fashioned. That's one reason I like going to Polo. The food is soooo good!

Grandma makes cookies and candy for the holidays, plus all the farm food. Because I get to take a little vacation from my regular food, we really watch my sugar levels closely, and we adjust how much insulin I take.

When we went to Polo at Thanksgiving, we were in a real big hurry. After I checked my blood sugar before breakfast, I somehow left my glucose monitor at home, and we didn't realize it until it was time to eat Thanksgiving dinner in Polo.

It was kind of an emergency. We hadn't done anything like that before. But my Aunt Dottie knows a boy in Polo who has diabetes. My dad and Uncle Pete drove into town and borrowed the boy's extra monitor so I could take tests. But the boy didn't have many extra test strips, so my dad and Uncle Pete had to find a drugstore that was open to buy some.

It was quite an adventure. But everything turned out fine.

When I was little, Dadders started calling me Stinky Good Breath. He likes nicknames. That's why we call my sisters Stretch and Niner.

Dadders would wake me up with a kiss in the morning. A lot of times, he knelt on the floor and put his head by mine on the bed. We'd talk, and he could smell my breath.

One of the signals that meant we had better get going was when Dadders would say something like, "Time to brush your teeth, Stinky Good Breath. It smells fine to me, but someone not in the family might take offense."

Pretty soon, Mommers and my sisters started calling me Stinky Good Breath, too. For some reason, I liked that name. When they called me it, I could blow stinky breath in their faces, and we'd laugh.

Hey stinky Good br

Dadders still calls me Stinky Good Breath once in a while. Usually, he does it when my blood sugar is high, and my breath smells "fruity."

When I have high blood sugar, Dadders says my breath smells a lot like when he used to wake me up in the morning and call me Stinky Good Breath. He wonders how long I was having high blood sugars before we found out about my diabetes.

It's sort of like when I got skinny, and was always thirsty, and wet the bed, and fainted on picture day. We never knew those were symptoms of diabetes until I was diagnosed.

Me and my trusty toothbrush.

ometimes, diabetes can be stressful, like when I forgot to bring my glucose monitor to Grandma and Grandpa's at Thankgiving. It's stressful when I get a craving to eat candy, too, and Mommers and Dadders don't think I should eat any.

Another time was when Copper chewed up my injector. Actually, he chewed it up twice. The first time, it wasn't so bad. The second time, though, my dad got really mad, just like the second time that Copper chewed up Stretch's retainer.

Grandpa B.

Copper.

Grandma B.

Retainers and injectors are pretty expensive, and Dadders doesn't like to waste money. When Copper chewed up my injector the second time, it was on a Saturday when I was going to sleep over at Grandma and Grandpa B's. My dad said I wouldn't be able to spend the night there now because I wouldn't be able to give myself shots, and Grandma and Grandpa don't know how to give them.

I cried really hard. I got really mad at Copper, even though it wasn't his fault because he only chews up things when we don't put them away.

I called up Grandpa and explained what happened. He felt very bad, too. Later, Grandpa called up my dad and said he'd like to buy me another injector. At first, my dad said, no, I'd have to buy my own new injector, or else I'd never learn. They talked some more. Then dad left the house.

He came back later with a new injector, and I got to stay at Grandma and Grandpa's that night.

When I apologized to Copper for getting mad at him, I heard Dadders ask Mommers, "Why do grandchildren get along so well with their grand-parents?"

"I don't know," Mommers said.

"Because they have a common enemy," Dadders said.

Then they laughed.

One of the best things about this year has been the Diabetes Walk. It raises money to find a cure for diabetes.

Mommers, Dadders, Stretch, Niner and I all walked. Some people brought their dogs, too, but Copper isn't trained good enough for crowds like that. He's too excitable, and we didn't even think of bringing him.

The walk is something everybody in my family said they wanted to do for me and my diabetes. So, I felt pretty neat and special about it, kind of like I was having an extra birthday.

It would have been too far for Copper to walk, anyway. He's a little dog, and it was 6.2 miles. I even really got tired and had sore feet. My best friend, Aimers (that's my nickname for Amy), walked with me. She doesn't have diabetes, but she got some pledges from her neighbors to support me. We had a blast, even though we came in about last place. But it wasn't a race.

Me and Aimers.

Dadders didn't walk right with us, but he sort of kept an eye on us. He said Aimers and I were twiddling too much and that we couldn't walk and talk at the same time. We stopped a lot. That's why we were so far behind.

By the time we finished, back at the park where we started, Niner and some friends she walked with were lost. Dadders looked for them. He even drove the van back over the course while we ate the picnic lunch that was served at the park.

Niner and her friends showed up while we were eating. They'd been playing somewhere in the park all the time, but we hadn't seen them.

When Dadders came back, he was kind of mad, but not too bad.

ur group was one of the biggest in the whole walk. Besides our family and friends, my teacher Mrs. Gerald and my gym teacher, Mrs. Rogers, walked. Mrs. Gerald brought her son, Aaron, who's a first grader, and Mrs. Rogers pushed her baby in a stroller the whole way.

Most of the kids in my mom's class walked, too. She invited her students to walk as kind of a class project for physical fitness and to learn about diabetes. A lot of them brought their moms and dads and brothers and sisters. We had sort of a mob.

Dadders got T-shirts from our credit union for everyone who walked on our team. The shirts kind of kept us all together at the start – until some of the boys ran off ahead to try to win first place, and Aimers and I started twiddling.

Before the walk started, we had a group picture taken. There were 32 of us in the photo, but even more people showed up for our team after the picture was taken. There we so many people on our team that I didn't even know them all!

Dadders and I sent a bunch of letters to people before the walk. I wrote my own letter and made copies, and Dadders wrote a form letter to go along with mine. We sent them to relatives, friends, companies my mom and dad do business with, and just about everyone else we could think of who might be interested.

In my letter, I said that donations were just a suggestion and that no one should feel pressured to make a pledge. We heard back from just about everyone. I couldn't believe it when Uncle Lonny and Aunt Lou sent a check for $500, and so did a company my dad works with.

It was awesome! We were one of the top teams because we raised more than $2,000 to find a cure for diabetes!

A few weeks ago, a big package came for me in the mail. There was a trophy with my name on it from the Juvenile Diabetes Research Foundation and a plaque with the picture of our team. I put the trophy and the plaque in my room. I'm proud of them because they're the first real awards I ever received.

I really don't mind my diabetes. A lot of people say that I'm doing great.

I'm trying to be patient, waiting for the people who are looking for a cure. I'm hoping they find it quickly. Until they do, I'm going to try very hard to take care of my diabetes. I don't want to have any permanent damage before they find the cure.

Thank you for taking the time to read my story. I'll probably add on to it after this year's walk, just to let you know how everything is going.

Dadders says we now have a tradition to uphold.